HEATHCLIFF
RIDES AGAIN

HEATHCLIFF

HEATHCLIFF RIDES AGAIN

BY GEORGE GATELY

tempo books

GROSSET & DUNLAP
Publishers • New York

"YOU PHONED FOR AN EXTERMINATOR?"

"TAKE ME TO YOUR LEADER!"

"LOOK OUT!...DON'T GET CRUMBS IN HIS BED!"

"I'LL DO THE JUDGING, IF YOU DON'T MIND!"

"WHAT'S THIS BILL FOR FIFTY-FIVE DOLLARS FROM THE CARPENTER ?...

...REPAIRS ON HEATHCLIFF'S SCRATCHING POST !!"

"I'M IN LUCK!... NO SIGN OF THAT
BOTTLE-BREAKING, SCHEMING, CONNIVING...

....HEATHCLIFF!!"

"I'M AFRAID YOUR CAT DOESN'T LIKE IT HERE!"

"WHY, THANK YOU!"

"I'LL SHOW YOU PUNKS HOW TO PLAY
FOOTBALL!...GET ME A HELMET."

"SOMEONE'S BEEN FOOLING AROUND WITH THE STUFFED BIRD EXHIBIT!"

"WOTTA YA IN FOR, KID?"

"OH, GOODNESS ME!... I SEE BABY IS HUNGRY."

"CARE FOR A CANTER THROUGH THE PARK?"

"HE DUMPS EVERY GARBAGE CAN EXCEPT THE FINSTERS!"

"THE FINSTERS ARE VEGETARIANS."

"IS HE BACK AGAIN ?!"

"YOU GAVE IT TO THE DELIVERY BOY?!!...
WE DON'T HAVE A DELIVERY BOY!!"

"JUST CATCH THEM!...DON'T TRAIN THEM!"

"I SHOULD BE ABLE TO FIX THIS....
THERE'S MORE THAN ONE WAY TO SKIN A CAT!"

"PARDON ME."

"OH, OH!"

"HE DOESN'T TAKE SUGAR.....
JUST LOTS AND LOTS OF CREAM!"

"YOU'VE GOT HEATHCLIFF?...
WHAT MISCHIEF HAS HE
BEEN IN NOW?"

"BAIL IS SET AT $15,000!"

"LOOK WHO'S LEFT HIMSELF ON OUR DOORSTEP."

"I WAS READING HEATHCLIFF SOME OF YOUR OLD LOVE LETTERS."

"STOP, THIEF!"

"WELL, AT LEAST HE'S A GOOD SPORT ABOUT NOT WINNING!"

"I GIVE UP!...I CAN'T GET RUFUS INTO THE TUB!"

"ONE OF OUR SHARKS IS MISSING!"

"THERE'S SOMETHING MIGHTY SUSPICIOUS ABOUT THIS NOTE!"

"I TELL YOU, HE'S IN HERE SOMEPLACE...
HIS GETAWAY CAR IS PARKED OUT FRONT!"

"ANOTHER COMPLAINT!... HE'S TANGLED WITH A RUSSIAN WOLFHOUND!"

"THAT LITTLE FELLOW IN THE CAT SUIT WON A BUNDLE!"

"WATCH OUT!...HIS MOOD RING IS TURNING A NASTY COLOR!"

"HE'S A GARBAGE DUMPER'S GARBAGE DUMPER!"

8-27

"HE'S A PRIZE-WINNING DOBERMAN PINSCHER."

"THAT'S PINSCHER, NOT PINCHER!"

"BUT GRANDMA, HEATHCLIFF WON'T CHASE A MOUSE WHILE HE'S ON HIS MILK BREAK!"

"WATCH THIS GUY AND YOU'LL LEARN SOMETHING!"

"REMOVE YOUR HAT, PLEASE... I CAN'T SEE."

"HE'S A VERY EFFICIENT MASCOT!"

"HE WON'T COME OUT... HE'S TIRED OF BEING
JUST ANOTHER HANDSOME FACE."

"POOR BABY!...DID-UMS GET A BOO BOO?"

"I'LL HANDLE THIS!"

"BONGO!...WHERE ARE YOU, BONGO ?!"

" NOW, WATCH THE BIRDIE, SON ... "

"DO IT, HEATHCLIFF!"   "DON'T DO IT, HEATHCLIFF!"

"HE'S A VERY POOR LOSER!"

"...AND INHABITED BY STRANGE, FURRY CREATURES!..."

"HE DOESN'T SEEM TO MIND A MILK BATH!"

"I RECOMMEND THAT YOU TAKE HIM TO ANOTHER VET... J.B. FLEAGENDORF."

"I NEVER DID LIKE FLEAGENDORF!"

"WELL, THAT'S SHOW BIZ!"

10-6

"LET ME IN!...LET ME IN!"

"BOOK HIM!"

"I'M NOT READY FOR YOU YET!"

"DO IT, HEATHCLIFF!"   "DON'T DO IT, HEATHCLIFF!"

"HOLD IT, WISE GUY!"

"HE'S GOT SOMEBODY NEW SINGING BASS!"

"NO THANK YOU!... I'VE ALREADY EATEN!!"

"MISS, DID YOU LOSE A MEGAPHONE?"

"COMFY?"

"DID YOU KNOW HEATHCLIFF'S GOT MONEY
IN HIS MATTRESS?!"

"THAT'S FUNNY... I THOUGHT IT WAS *YOUR*
STOMACH RUMBLING!"

"I SAW YOU SWIPE THAT FISH!...NOW, WHERE IS IT?"

"LOOK!...THERE GOES THE TUNA FLEET!"

"DID I HEAR THE FLAMINGO SCREAM?!"

"SHOULD THE MASCOT DINE WITH THE TEAM?"

"HE LIKES TO BUILD A NICE WARM FIRE
ON THESE CHILLY DAYS."

"LET'S SEE...WE GIVE FIVE DOLLARS TO THE MAILMAN...
FIVE DOLLARS TO THE SANITATION MEN..."

"...AND, OH YES...FIVE DOLLARS TO THE DOGCATCHER."

"SAY!...THAT LOOKS LIKE SPIKE!...
HOW DID YOU DO THAT?!"

"THE OCTOPUS WILL DEFEND ITSELF BY
EMITTING A CLOUD OF BLACK INK."

"HE DOESN'T LIKE HIS NEW PILLS!"

"MAYBE HEATHCLIFF SHOULDN'T GO OUT ON SUCH A COLD NIGHT!"

"THERE'S YOUR TROUBLE!"

"YOU DON'T CARE FOR 'PINKY, THE PEPPY
LITTLE PUPPY'?"

"MUGGSY FABER HIT HIM IN THE HEAD WITH A SNOWBALL."

"*THIS* IS NOT A SCRATCHING POST!"

"MAY I HAVE A VOLUNTEER FROM THE AUDIENCE, PLEASE?"

"THAT'S A BEAUTIFUL NEW TRUCK!...
JUST LISTEN TO THAT ENGINE PURR!"

"THE ENGINE ISN'T RUNNING."

"WHAT'S HE DOING WITH MY SNOOZE-ALARM?"

"IT'S THE ZOO... SOMETHING ABOUT A PEACOCK!"

"I COULDN'T RECOGNIZE HIM... HE HAD
A STOCKING OVER HIS FACE!"

"SCRAM, YOU PHONEY!"

"WELL, SO MUCH FOR KISSING BABIES!"

"YOU WOULDN'T BELIEVE THE STUFF HE FINDS IN A GARBAGE CAN!!"

"I DON'T THINK HE APPRECIATED YOUR LITTLE JOKE!"

"I'M MAKING A SANDWICH...DO YOU WANT
ANYTHING, HEATHCLIFF?"

"WE'RE ALL SET....NOW IF WE JUST HAD
A COSTUME FOR SPIKE!"

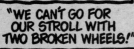

"WE CAN'T GO FOR
OUR STROLL WITH
TWO BROKEN WHEELS!"

"EVERY ONCE IN AWHILE SOMETHING MAKES HIM BREAK INTO A NERVOUS RASH!"

"HMMMM...?!"

"GET OUT OF THAT BIRD FEEDER!"

"WE GET AN OCCASIONAL MOUSE IN THE BASEMENT."

"WHAT'S YOUR HOROSCOPE FOR TODAY?"

"AVOID CONFRONTATION WITH ONE WHO IS SMALL, BUT WISER THAN YOURSELF."

"YOUR CAT'S QUITE A COMEDIAN!"

"WHAT'S A CAT DOING ON A SKI-LIFT?!"

"CLEAN-UP DAY."

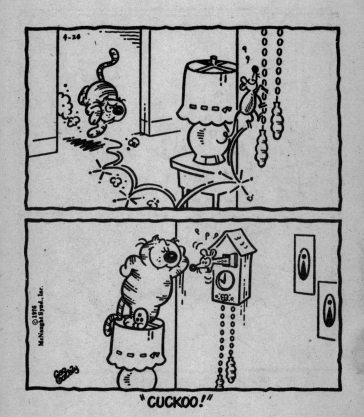

"CUCKOO!"

"C'MON, HEATHCLIFF!...DON'T DISTURB THE BATS!"

"YOU'RE GIVING THE PLACE A BAD NAME!"

"HE GOT SOMEONE TO DO THE LYRICS!"

"WHAT HAPPENED TO ALL THE MONEY ?!"

"DON'T DO ANYTHING
I WOULDN'T DO!"

"HAVE YOU SEEN HEATHCLIFF?...HE WAS CHASING A SKUNK!"

"YOUR NE'ER-DO-WELL BROTHER IS AT THE DOOR."

"HE DOESN'T WANT ANY PICTURES TAKEN."

"IT'S NOT A MOUSE, HEATHCLIFF!...IT'S A CHIHUAHUA!"

4-21   ©1976
McNaught Synd., Inc.